ENGLISH

KEY STAGE 3 LEVELS 4 – 7

READING PAPER 1

Remember

To complete this test you will need a watch or clock to time yourself.

Sit at a table in a quiet place.

The next five pages contain three extracts on the theme of 'Mars'.

- You should spend 15 minutes reading these extracts before turning to the questions on pages 7 to 12.

- After you have read the extracts through, you have one hour to answer the questions.

- There are spaces in which you should write your answers, but you can use extra paper if you need it.

- The paper has 32 marks in total.

H.G. Wells' novel 'War of the Worlds' tells the story of a Martian invasion of Earth. The Martians build weapons designed to kill humans, described by the writer as "vast spider-like machines, nearly a hundred feet high, capable of the speed of an express train, and able to shoot out a beam of intense heat." The following extract describes an attack by these 'Heat-Rays' near the River Thames in London.

Martian Attack

At that I ducked at once under water, and, holding my breath until movement was an agony, blundered painfully ahead under the surface as long as I could. The water was in a **tumult** about me, and rapidly growing hotter.

When for a moment I raised my head to take breath and throw the hair and water from my eyes, the steam was rising in a whirling white fog that at first hid the Martians altogether. The noise was deafening. Then I saw them dimly, colossal figures of grey, magnified by the mist. They had passed by me, and two were stooping over the frothing, tumultuous ruins of their comrade.

The third and fourth stood beside him in the water, one perhaps two hundred yards from me, the other towards Laleham. The generators of the Heat-Rays waved high, and the hissing beams **smote** down this way and that.

The air was full of sound, a deafening and confusing conflict of noises – the **clangorous** din of the Martians, the crash of falling houses, the thud of trees, fences, sheds flashing into flame, and the crackling and roaring of fire. Dense black smoke was leaping up to mingle with the steam from the river, and as the Heat-Ray went to and fro over Weybridge its impact was marked by flashes of **incandescent** white, that gave place at once to a smoky dance of **lurid** flames. The nearer houses still stood intact, awaiting their fate, shadowy, faint and **pallid** in the steam, with the fire behind them going to and fro.

For a moment perhaps I stood there, breast-high in the almost boiling water, dumbfounded at my position, hopeless of escape. Through the **reek** I could see the people who had been with me in the river scrambling out of the water through the reeds, like little frogs hurrying through grass from the advance of a man, or running to and fro in utter dismay on the towing path.

Reading Paper 1

Then suddenly the white flashes of the Heat-Ray came leaping towards me. The houses caved in as they dissolved at its touch, and darted out flames; the trees changed to fire with a roar. The Ray flickered up and down the towing path, licking off the people who ran this way and that, and came down to the water's edge not fifty yards from where I stood. It swept across the river to Shepperton, and the water in its track rose in a boiling **weal** crested with steam. I turned shoreward.

In another moment the huge wave, well-nigh at the boiling-point had rushed upon me. I screamed aloud, and scalded, half blinded, agonised, I staggered through the leaping, hissing water towards the shore. Had my foot stumbled, it would have been the end. I fell helplessly, in full sight of the Martians, upon the broad, bare gravelly spit that runs down to mark the angle of the Wey and Thames. I expected nothing but death.

I have a dim memory of the foot of a Martian coming down within a score of yards of my head, driving straight into the loose gravel, whirling it this way and that and lifting again; of a long suspense, and then of the four carrying the debris of their comrade between them, now clear and then presently faint through a veil of smoke, receding interminably, as it seemed to me, across a vast space of river and meadow. And then, very slowly, I realised that by a miracle I had escaped.

tumult – uproar   **smote** – struck   **clangorous** – noisy

incandescent – glowing white-hot   **lurid** – bright, glaring

pallid – pale   **reek** – smoke   **weal** – wave

Human exploration of Mars has been a subject that has fascinated men and women for many years. There are no firm plans to send astronauts to Mars at present, but it could happen in your lifetime. The piece of writing that follows is fictional, set in perhaps the not too distant future...

A speech to the Society for the Human Exploration of Mars (S.H.E.M.), by Martin Embury, President of the Society.

Welcome, ladies and gentlemen, to the annual conference of SHEM, held for the sixth year running here in Birmingham.

For years the red planet has occupied both our waking thoughts and our night-time dreams. Men have written novels about it, composed music, made films in an attempt to capture its mysterious nature. But now our dreams are about to become reality. I have an opportunity to lay before you today, an opportunity that is both exciting and hazardous.

For the last ten years NASA* has been working on a project, a project so important and so shrouded in secrecy that details have only been given to a small number of organisations. Ladies and gentlemen, I can reveal to you today that SHEM has been privileged as one of the chosen few to which NASA has shared its most closely guarded plans.

As you all know, up to the present time the only possible way of travelling to Mars, over two hundred million kilometres away, has been by chemically propelled rockets. The most advanced of these designs have, up to now, been at the forefront of space technology, the Ferraris of interplanetary travel. They would take only six months to fly to Mars, the mere pulse of a heartbeat compared to the craft of ten years ago.

Yet even these super-rockets are too slow for safe travel to Mars. The fuel required for the journey would take up most of the volume of the spacecraft; there would not be enough to return to Earth should the flight have to be aborted. How many of us would volunteer for such a mission? No government would risk sending its citizens into the dark deserts of space under such conditions.

Yet suddenly there is fresh hope for those passionate about exploring this newest of worlds. NASA has unveiled the prototype of a spacecraft, of a kind never seen before, a rocket with a plasma engine which uses super-heated gas as fuel. It will take far less time to reach Mars and there will be sufficient fuel to return.

And this is where you come in. NASA are beginning to train a team of astronauts to pilot this rocket, a team of highly skilled men and women who will be the first human beings to set foot on Martian soil. They want to add to this team one ordinary man or woman – it could be you, me, any one of us sitting here today. The chosen person will be extensively trained over a number of years so that he or she can play an active part in the mission.

However, the real role of this person is to be a representative of common humanity, the ordinary man or woman with a passion for space, for exploration and for the unknown. It will not be an easy decision to make. You will have to leave loved ones far behind, the furthest Man has ever travelled. There is a chance you will not return. But there is every chance that you will contribute something priceless to history.

Competition for this place will be tough. Many, many people will apply, from all nations and all walks of life. How proud we would all be if the person finally chosen came from SHEM, which has devoted itself for so many years to Mars, our closest neighbour, for too long just out of reach.

* NASA : National Aeronautics and Space Administration (U.S.A.)

Imagine the typical astronaut. You are probably picturing a man or woman of about 30, supremely fit, expertly trained, at the peak of their physical and mental powers. Such a superhuman, you feel, would be able to withstand the hazards of a mission far into space, even to Mars. Think again. Some scientists believe that the dangers to physical and mental health posed by a return trip to Mars mean that it would be foolhardy to send even the fittest of our species on such a mission.

So what sort of advice should be given to those about to set off on a trip to Mars?

SPACE TRAVEL – A HEALTH WARNING

Early days

In the first three days after the launch your body will be adjusting to the very different conditions in the small spacecraft. You will be weightless as you leave Earth's gravity behind. This may affect your inner ear, causing confusion and dizziness. The rhythm of your heart may become disturbed. These changes, together with the different diet, may make you feel sick or even vomit. And this is just the start.

The voyage continues

Over the long journey to Mars your muscles are likely to become weaker because of lack of exercise in the cramped capsule. Your bones will start to lose calcium. More seriously, as more time is spent under weightless conditions, something called the 'cephalad shift' occurs. Instead of your body fluids being pulled downwards by gravity they will gradually move upwards to your chest and head. Your body will change shape: you will develop a puffy face and stick-like legs. As a result, receptors in your heart and arteries mistakenly sense that you contain too much fluid and send signals to the kidneys to urinate. The combination of extra urine and loss of calcium from your bones will increase the risk of suffering from kidney stones, easily treatable on Earth, but a potentially dangerous condition while floating through space with no access to a hospital.

In addition to the physical hardship, you will experience the mental stress of being shut up for months on end in a tiny capsule with the same four or five people. The effects of this are much harder to predict. At best you may suffer from mood swings; at worst panic attacks and depression may set in. You will probably be longing to arrive at your destination, but your problems have only just begun.

On Mars

The Martian day is 24 hours and 38 minutes. The light is dim and red as opposed to the bright blue light of Earth. The average temperature is minus 60 degrees. Adapting to life on Mars may cause all sorts of problems, perhaps the most important of which is the disruption in your sleep patterns. You are likely to become very tired and disorientated. This may affect your ability to do your job safely, much as an exhausted or drunk driver is impaired when handling a car. You would also have to cope with frequent storms of silicon dust which can damage your lungs and explosions on the surface of the sun which release lethal radiation.

All this is temporary however. At the end of a few weeks on Mars you will begin the long trip back to the familiar comforts of home. But what then?

Back down to Earth

Perhaps intensive training can help astronauts to cope with the effects of their time away from Earth. However, no-one knows the psychological pressures you will suffer, because no-one has yet made such a trip. You will have left everything familiar, everyone you love, all of human history far behind. Who knows how you will react on your return?

Reading Paper 1

Questions 1 to 4 are about the extract from 'War of the Worlds'

1 (a) From the first sentence, write down one word which suggests how the narrator ('I') is moving through the water.

_____

(b) Explain what this means.

_____

_____

2 In the fourth paragraph the writer describes the scene: " The air was full of sound, a deafening and confusing conflict of noises – the clangorous din of the Martians, the crash of falling houses, the thud of trees, fences, sheds flashing into flame, and the crackling and roaring of fire."

Explain two ways in which this sentence brings the scene to life for the reader. Use a quotation from the sentence to back up each of your comments.

• _____

_____

_____

_____

• _____

_____

_____

3 This text is written in the first person (using 'I'). Give one reason why this helps to make the writing exciting.

_____

_____

_____

Reading Paper 1   TOTAL [ ]

4 How does the whole piece of writing emphasise the contrast between the Martians and the humans?

You should comment on how the writer's use of words and phrases

(a) makes the Martians sound powerful;
(b) makes the humans sound weak;
(c) emphasises the differences between them in any other ways.

_____

_____

_____

_____

_____

_____

_____

_____

_____

_____

_____

_____

_____

_____

_____

_____

_____

_____

_____

5 marks

Questions 5 to 8 are about Martin Embury's speech on pages 4 and 5.

5 Martin Embury is about to reveal an exciting opportunity to his audience. Explain two ways in which the first paragraph of his speech would make his audience want to listen.

Back up each explanation with a quotation from the first paragraph.

- _____
_____
_____
_____

- _____
_____
_____

6 (a) In the third paragraph the speaker explains how fast spacecraft can travel nowadays. Find a metaphor which emphasises this.

_____

b) How does the metaphor emphasise the speed of these rockets?

_____
_____
_____

7 (a) Identify the phrase in the third paragraph that makes space seem dangerous.

_____

b) What other effects does this phrase have on your feelings about space?

_____
_____
_____

TOTAL

9

8 How does the speaker persuade his listeners that travel to Mars is an exciting prospect?

You should comment on:

(a) the way in which the whole speech is organised;
(b) the different ways in which the speaker tries to involve his audience;
(c) the words and phrases he uses to describe space travel and the planet Mars.

_____

_____

_____

_____

_____

_____

_____

_____

_____

_____

_____

_____

_____

_____

_____

_____

_____

_____

_____

5 marks

Questions 9 to 12 are about the article 'Space Travel – A Health Warning'.

9 Explain one way in which the introduction to this article (boxed in bold type) is effective as an opening. Back up your explanation with a quotation from this paragraph.

_____

_____

_____

_____

1 mark

10 (a) Each paragraph of the article is headed by a subtitle.
Give one way in which this helps the organisation of the text as a whole.

_____

_____

1 mark

(b) How is each paragraph ended?

_____

_____

1 mark

(c) What is the purpose of this?

_____

_____

1 mark

11 The article is written in the second person ('you').
What is the effect of this on the reader?

_____

_____

_____

_____

1 mark

TOTAL

12 What do you learn about the writer's viewpoint in the text as a whole?

Decide whether the following statements are true or false and then write T for True or F for False in the box provided. The first one has been done for you.

The writer feels that most astronauts would cope well with the pressures of a trip to Mars.

| F |

The writer believes that the worst problems will be experienced in the first few days of the mission.

| |

The writer is more certain about the effects of such a trip on the body than on the mind.

| |

Question 13 is about Martin Embury's speech and the article 'Space Travel – A Health Warning'.

13 The two passages, Martin Embury's speech and 'Space Travel – A Health Warning', have their own purposes, similar in some ways, different in others.

Complete the table below giving one purpose for each text and one word which describes the language or tone of each text.

	Martin Embury's speech	Space Travel – A Health Warning
Purpose		
Language or tone		

ENGLISH

KEY STAGE 3   LEVELS 4 – 7

WRITING PAPER 1

Remember

To complete this test you will need a watch or clock to time yourself.

Sit at a table in a quiet place.

This test contains two writing tasks.

- It is 1 hour and 15 minutes long.

- You should spend 45 minutes on Section 1. This is the longer writing task and is worth 30 marks. We provide a planning sheet but you will need to use sheets of paper or an exercise book to complete the task.

- You should spend 30 minutes on Section 2. This is the shorter writing task. It is worth 20 marks (including 4 marks for spelling).

- Spend the first 15 minutes planning your answer to Section 1 on the planning page provided.

Section 1 Longer writing task

You and a group of friends wish to hire a local hall for a birthday party. You have to apply to the Town Council for permission. Just before you do so, a report appears in the local paper. Here is an extract:

TEENAGE TROUBLE

The Council is considering banning groups of young people from hiring the hall in the town centre after a number of complaints from those living nearby. These were some of the comments made:

"The noise was terrible – loud music playing and the party-goers shouting as they left. I couldn't get my baby to sleep."

" The area around the hall was littered with rubbish."

" Hiring the hall out to teenagers simply encourages under-age drinking, smoking and other anti-social habits. It shouldn't be allowed."

Write a letter to Mr. J. Osbourne, Chair of the Recreation Committee, persuading him that you and your friends should be allowed to hire the hall.

(30 marks)

Section 1 Longer writing task
PLANNING PAGE

Use this page to plan your work. It will not be marked.

- How you will overcome the problem of disturbing local residents

- How you will ensure there is no rubbish left in the surrounding area

- How you will discourage anti-social and illegal behaviour

- Any other points to convince the Council that you are a responsible group of young people

Section 2 Shorter writing task

Your local Tourist Information Centre is planning to produce a brochure recommending places of interest to young people in your area. The following note comes through your door:

CAN YOU HELP?

We want to put together a brochure of places to go for young people of different ages. Could you help us by writing an entry? You can choose to describe a place that you enjoy visiting now, or one that you think would appeal to younger children. It could be a zoo, a park, a beach, a museum, a sports centre, a café or simply a place in the town or country. Anywhere that you have enjoyed visiting is fine.

Please include the following:

• A brief description of your chosen place.

• The age group it would appeal to most.

• Reasons why it is worth visiting.

Any practical information needed – is it free or do you have to pay? Do you need any particular clothing or equipment? (Don't worry if you can't remember exact details about entrance fees or opening times, as we can add those when we put the brochure together.)

Write the brochure entry describing your chosen place.

(20 marks)   (including 4 for spelling)

ENGLISH

KEY STAGE 3 LEVELS 4 – 7

SHAKESPEARE PAPER: MACBETH

Note for you and your parents

Your school will choose one of three Shakespeare plays to study for the test. For 2005, these are 'Macbeth', 'Much Ado About Nothing' and 'Henry V'. You will study the whole play, but with particular reference to two scenes or extracts from scenes which are chosen by the examination authority. The reading task on the test paper will be based on these scenes, which change from year to year.

The practice task on these pages is an example of the sort of question you can expect whichever play you are studying and whichever scenes have been set for the test.

Remember

• Sit at a table in a quiet place.

• You can spend as long as you like reading through the extracts, then you have 45 minutes to write your answer.

• The test has a total score of 18 marks.

MACBETH

Act 1 Scene 7, lines 28 to 82   Act 2 Scene 2 (whole scene)

Read the extracts carefully before you start writing your answer to the question. The question tests how well you know and understand the play. It is important to refer to the two extracts to support your answer.

Here is your task:

You have been given these extracts to direct for a class performance.

How would you advise the actor playing Lady Macbeth about the ways in which she could show her contrasting feelings, before and after Duncan's murder?

FIRST EXTRACT

MACBETH

Act 1 Scene 7, lines 28 – 82

In this extract, Lady Macbeth persuades Macbeth to continue with their plan to murder King Duncan.

Enter LADY MACBETH

MACBETH	How now! what news?
LADY MACBETH	He has almost supp'd: why have you left the chamber?
MACBETH	Hath he ask'd for me?
LADY MACBETH	Know you not he has? 30

MACBETH   We will proceed no further in this business:
He hath honour'd me of late; and I have bought
Golden opinions from all sorts of people,
Which would be worn now in their newest gloss,
Not cast aside so soon.   35

LADY MACBETH   Was the hope drunk
Wherein you dress'd yourself? hath it slept since?
And wakes it now, to look so green and pale
At what it did so freely? From this time
Such I account thy love. Art thou afeard
To be the same in thine own act and valour   40
As thou art in desire? Wouldst thou have that
Which thou esteem'st the ornament of life,
And live a coward in thine own esteem,
Letting 'I dare not' wait upon 'I would,'
Like the poor cat i' the adage?   45

MACBETH   Prithee, peace:
I dare do all that may become a man;
Who dares do more is none.

Shakespeare: Macbeth

LADY MACBETH   What beast was't, then,
                         That made you break this enterprise to me?
                         When you durst do it, then you were a man;
                         And, to be more than what you were, you would   50
                         Be so much more the man. Nor time nor place
                         Did then adhere, and yet you would make both:
                         They have made themselves, and that their fitness now
                         Does unmake you. I have given suck, and know
                         How tender 'tis to love the babe that milks me: 55
                         I would, while it was smiling in my face,
                         Have pluck'd my nipple from his boneless gums,
                         And dash'd the brains out, had I so sworn as you
                         Have done to this.

MACBETH   If we should fail?

LADY MACBETH   We fail!
                         But screw your courage to the sticking-place,   60
                         And we'll not fail. When Duncan is asleep–
                         Whereto the rather shall his day's hard journey
                         Soundly invite him–his two chamberlains
                         Will I with wine and wassail so convince
                         That memory, the warder of the brain,   65
                         Shall be a fume, and the receipt of reason
                         A limbeck only: when in swinish sleep
                         Their drenched natures lie as in a death,
                         What cannot you and I perform upon
                         The unguarded Duncan? what not put upon   70
                         His spongy officers, who shall bear the guilt
                         Of our great quell?

MACBETH   Bring forth men-children only;
                         For thy undaunted mettle should compose
                         Nothing but males. Will it not be received,
                         When we have mark'd with blood those sleepy two   75
                         Of his own chamber and used their very daggers,
                         That they have done't?

LADY MACBETH   Who dares receive it other,
                         As we shall make our griefs and clamour roar
                         Upon his death?

MACBETH   I am settled, and bend up
                         Each corporal agent to this terrible feat.   80
                         Away, and mock the time with fairest show:
                         False face must hide what the false heart doth know.

Exeunt

Shakespeare: Macbeth

SECOND EXTRACT

MACBETH
Act 2 Scene 2 (whole scene)

In this scene, Macbeth kills Duncan in his bedroom, offstage. He and his wife talk about what happened in the bedroom and the audience sees their reactions to the murder.

Enter LADY MACBETH

LADY MACBETH That which hath made them drunk hath made me bold;
What hath quench'd them hath given me fire. Hark! Peace!
It was the owl that shriek'd, the fatal bellman,
Which gives the stern'st good-night. He is about it:
The doors are open; and the surfeited grooms   5
Do mock their charge with snores: I have drugg'd their possets,
That death and nature do contend about them,
Whether they live or die.

MACBETH   [Within] Who's there? what, ho!

LADY MACBETH Alack, I am afraid they have awaked,
And 'tis not done. The attempt and not the deed   10
Confounds us. Hark! I laid their daggers ready;
He could not miss 'em. Had he not resembled
My father as he slept, I had done't.

Enter MACBETH

                             My husband!

MACBETH   I have done the deed. Didst thou not hear a noise?

LADY MACBETH I heard the owl scream and the crickets cry.   15
Did not you speak?

MACBETH   When?

LADY MACBETH   Now.

MACBETH   As I descended?

LADY MACBETH Ay.
Extract continues after Answer Section

Shakespeare: Macbeth

Marking the Reading papers

The mark schemes used to mark the Reading papers are very complex and the answers that follow are a guide only. You do not need to have used the exact words given here to gain a mark. It is a good idea to discuss your answers with someone else and decide together whether you have answered correctly. Examiners will award marks for a range of acceptable responses.

ANSWERS TO READING PAPER 1

Q   **Marks**

1 (a) 'blundered'   1
  (b) Any of the following: moving blindly; moving clumsily; unsure of direction.   1

2 Any two of the following: use of onomatopoeic (sound) words; use of alliteration to emphasise   1
  the sounds and sights ('flashing into flame'); use of complex sentence with many dependent clauses
  to give sense of everything happening at once.
  Two relevant quotations to back up comments.   1

3 Any of the following: makes story more personal; makes it more exciting because reader identifies
  with narrator; narrator's viewpoint becomes reader's.   1

4 Martians are in control and people are helpless and panic-stricken 'running to and fro in utter
  dismay'. The narrator is trapped – 'hopeless of escape'. Martians are 'colossal' and seem even bigger
  and more frightening because partly hidden by mist. The people are like 'little frogs'. Martians have
  fire in their control with all its destructive force. Houses are 'dissolved' by the Heat Rays.
  Humans can do nothing to halt them. Heat Ray described as 'licking off' the people –
  emphasises how easy the destruction is.   5
  (To get full marks you need to give a full answer with appropriate quotation to support
  your comments.)

5 Any **two** of the following: he talks about the fascination people have for Mars; he uses contrast
  (eg. 'exciting and hazardous', 'waking thoughts and night-time dreams'); he uses repetition ('dreams',
  'opportunity) he uses a common rhetorical device (a technique used by public speakers) called
  'groups of three' ('written novels… composed music, made films');
  he delays saying what the 'opportunity' is, which builds suspense.
  (A word or phrase should be quoted to support each of the two points.)   2

6 'the Ferraris of interplanetary travel' or 'the mere pulse of a heartbeat'   1
  The rocket is compared to a fast car to give a sense of its speed which is more likely to be in the
  reader's experience.   1
  or
  The flight to Mars is compared to the flicker of a heartbeat, an exaggeration which emphasises
  the speed of the spacecraft.

7 (a) 'the dark deserts of space'   1
  (b) lonely, frightening, empty, vast (any one of these)   1

8 He builds up suspense by waiting to reveal the exact nature of the 'opportunity' until half way
  through speech. He makes the audience feel privileged to be given details of NASA's latest plans.
  He often addresses his listeners directly ('ladies and gentlemen', 'you'). He uses a rhetorical question
  (a question that does not expect an answer) – 'How many of us would volunteer for such a mission?'
  to draw his listeners in and prepare them for the news that a new, safer method of travel has been
  invented. He makes it seem as if the person chosen for the mission will be very special and appeals
  to his audience's sense of pride. He makes Mars seem fascinating, mysterious and exciting.
  (To get full marks you need to give a full answer with appropriate quotation to support
  your comments.)   5

9 Any one of the following: appeals directly to the reader to get actively involved; makes
us build up a picture of a typical astronaut able to withstand all dangers and then knocks
it down ('Think again'); creates suspense because we want to know exactly what these
dangers are; ends with a question which makes us read on to get the answer.
A word or phrase should be quoted to support the point made.   1

10 (a) The subtitles are in chronological order (order of time) so help us to see how an
        astronaut's condition would deteriorate over time.   1
   (b) With a sentence which leads directly on to the next section.   1
   (c) To make the reader read on; to help with the 'flow' of the piece, to aid understanding.
       (any one of these)   1

11 Makes reader feel more personally involved – we identify with the astronaut.   1

12 F   1
    T   1

13 Embury's speech: Purpose – to excite **or** to inform   1
                             Language or tone – personal **or** persuasive **or** forceful **or** rhetorical   1
   Space Travel – A Health Warning:
                             Purpose – to inform **or** to warn **or** to argue a point of view   1
                             Language or tone – personal **or** persuasive **or** technical **or** detailed   1

Answers to Reading paper 2

1 Any of the following: heavily laden, straining, making a noise that suggests strain   1

2 Stage 2 : 'had to leave the sledge' **or** 'Evans came up again, but very slowly' **or**
             'Evans a long way astern' **or** 'we looked out, to see him still afar off'.   2
   Stage 3: 'on his knees with clothing disarrayed, hands uncovered and frostbitten,
             and a wild look in his eyes'.
   Stage 4: 'every sign of complete collapse'
   Stage 5: 'practically unconscious' **or** 'quite comatose'
   (Award half a mark for each correct stage.)

3 (a) 'It is a terrible thing to lose a companion in this way.'   1
   (b) 'Calm reflection shows that there could not have been a better ending to the terrible
       anxieties of the last week.' **or** 'Discussion of the situation at lunch yesterday shows us what
       a desperate pass we were in with a sick man on our hands at such a distance from home.'   1

4 (a) Any of the following: entries shorter; shorter sentences; connective words missed out.   1
   (b) Makes us realise that Scott was weak and close to death **or** makes us feel sympathy for
       Scott and his men.   1

5 Scott repeats the words 'terrible' and awful' often when describing the conditions. He describes
   the snow as an obstacle to the men at every step, 'clogging' their equipment and straining the sledge
   to breaking point. As the text is a diary, the language is sometimes plain and literal –'severe blizzard' –
   but sometimes descriptive – 'a scene of whirling drift. Scott describes Evans' gradual deterioration in
   detail and we get a sense of his conflicting feelings: the worry that Evans is holding the party back, his
   admiration for his bravery and endurance and his sadness at his death. Oates' sacrifice is described very
   movingly and with great admiration for his courage and selflessness. The change in style of the final
   entries suggests the growing desperation of the explorers' situation, but at the same time Scott shows
   a brave acceptance of their fate.
   (To get full marks you need to give a full answer with appropriate quotation to
   support your comments.)   5

6   He forgets to build a fire before eating his lunch. (You need the whole of this to get the mark.)   1

7   (a) 'he had laughed at him at the time' **or** 'Then he pulled on his mittens…and took the creek
       trail up the left fork' **or** 'This man did not know cold' or 'Possibly all the generations of his
       ancestry had been ignorant of cold…'
     (b) Any part of the section beginning, 'But the dog knew'… to 'this cold came'   2

8   He is relieved that he has lit a fire **or** he is proud of himself.
    He is ignorant of the real dangers **or** he is arrogant **or** complacent (self satisfied).   2

9   (a) Frozen solid, stopping his legs from moving.
    (b) Frozen solid in a tangled mess, difficult to undo.   2

10 The man's situation gradually gets more and more serious, but it takes him a long time to realise.
    The reader realises before he does. At the beginning he has no worries – he is reckless and complacent –
    'he chuckled at his foolishness'. The writer uses the contrast between his ignorance and the dog's
    wisdom to emphasis how dangerous his actions are. The man realises the situation is more serious
    when he gets his feet wet, but as soon as he lights the fire he becomes complacent and arrogant –
    'Any man who was a man could travel alone'. When snow blots out the fire he is shocked – has not
    thought ahead at all. The writer repeats the word 'cold' often for emphasis. The cold is described as a
    powerful force which has to be 'outwitted'. The writer uses actual temperatures to reinforce our sense
    of the extreme cold.
    (To get full marks you need to give a full answer with appropriate quotation to support your
    comments.)   5

11 Any two of the following: cutting, cold, cruel, continuous, unceasing .   2

12 (a) tension, anticipation
    (b) a feeling of pointlessness, depression   2

13 True, False, False, True   4

There are 32 marks in total for each Reading paper. If you want to convert your score into a NC level, use the chart below.
Remember that this is only a rough guide.

Mark	Level
25-32	7
20-24	6
13-19	5
7-12	4
0-6	Below 4

If you wish to get a rough idea of your overall Reading level, you should add the marks obtained in either Reading Paper 1
or Reading Paper 2 to the mark obtained in the Shakespeare paper 3. You should now have a mark out of 50. Use the chart
below to convert this to a NC level.

Mark	Level
35-50	7
28-34	6
18-27	5
12-17	4
0-11	Below 4

And finally, if you would like a rough idea of how your total marks convert to a NC level add your overall marks for
Reading to your marks for Writing to get a mark out of 100 and use the chart below.

Mark	Level
68-100	7
52-67	6
32-51	5
19-31	4
0-18	Below 4

Marking the Writing papers

On the following four pages you will find sample answers for each of the tasks on the two Writing papers. Each of these answers shows a different level of attainment. There are comments and marks attached so that you can see what is expected at each level. Look out for spelling and punctuation mistakes in the answers! Please remember that National Curriculum levels given are only approximate.

Sample answer for Writing paper 1: Longer task

Dear Mr. Osbourne,

I understand that there is some concern locally about the use of Crickley Hall by those under eighteen years old. While I understand those concerns, I would like you to consider an application to hire the hall by myself and a group of friends aged between thirteen and fourteen.

None of us wants to cause annoyance to local residents because of noise. I have spoken to those who live nearest the hall and it seems that this is only a problem if all the windows of the hall are open and the music goes on past 11pm. We will therefore ensure that the music played is at an acceptable volume and that only one window is open for ventilation at the back of the hall, where there are no houses. The party will finish at 11pm exactly, when the music will be switched off.

I hope that none of my friends would drop rubbish anywhere, let alone in their home town. However, a number of us have taken on the job of 'litter-pickers' and will clear both the hall and the surrounding courtyard when the party is over.

You may be thinking that this is all very well. This boy and his friends sound like a responsible group of young people. But what about those he doesn't know so well or can't control?

We have thought very hard about this and have come up with the following solution. Entrance to the party will be by ticket only. Two adults (my father and my uncle) will man the door and will turn away anyone without an invitation. They will also be on hand to enforce the 'no alcohol' and 'no smoking' rules in the unlikely event that this is needed.

The recent problems at Crickley Hall were caused by a few young people. Not all local teenagers are irresponsible. Many of us are responsible individuals who want to enjoy ourselves while respecting the wishes and rights of others. Not all of us should therefore be punished for the actions of a minority.

I hope that you will consider our application carefully and look forward to your reply.

Yours sincerely,

Tim Jones

The writer uses a range of sentence lengths and verb forms confidently, including the passive form ('The recent problems at Crickley Hall were caused by…')
A range of punctuation is used correctly.
There is a clear sense of audience and purpose, with reference to the different viewpoints of the Council, the young people and local residents. Ideas and information are confidently presented to persuade the reader. Problems are anticipated in order to present a solution. The whole piece is strongly argued and convincing. A range of persuasive techniques is used, eg. rhetorical questions ('But what about those…?') and repetition ('Not all…not all…').

This answer has been given a mark of 29/30, at the top of the Level 7 mark range.

Sample answer for Writing paper 1: Shorter task
This answer contains many errors.

Wishbrooks zoo

Wishbrooks zoo is an exiting place for children of all ages. You have to get there by car as it is in the middle of the contryside. It is open every day of the year exept Christmas Day.

Wishbrooks has lots of diferent animals ranging from chimps right down to tiny insects. They give you a lot of information about the animals on the cages so it is very intresting. My favrite animal is the marmoset because they are cute and often have babies that cling on to their mums.

After a while I somtimes get bored of all the animals but that doesn't matter because theres loads of other things to do you know. Like an assalt course, train rides, gift shops, a good café.

I hope you go and if you do go for the whole day as theres so much to see and do.

This is a clear description with a simple structure.
The beginning of the piece is appropriate but this is not consistent throughout the piece ('*theres loads of other things to do you know*').
The writer uses some varied sentence structure, but grammar and punctuation are not always secure ('*Like an assalt course, train rides, gift shops, a good café*')
Commonly used words are mostly spelled accurately, including there/their, but there are mistakes with more complex words (*assalt, favrite*).

This answer has been given a mark of 4/20, in the middle of the Level 4 mark range.

Sample answer for Writing paper 2: Longer task
This answer contains some errors.

Mary Murphy had travelled over the world looking for big cats but this was the strangest case she had ever heard of. The man on the other end of the phone sounded scared out of his life.
"Slow down please," she said trying to sound calm. "Tell me exactly what you saw again."
Ed Pitley started his story again with a deep breath but he still sounded paniked.
"It was a huge black shape," he said breathlesly. " I thought it was coming for my sheep but then it ran away along the fence, and jumped over it at the end. It sent shivers up and down my spine."

When Ed finished giving her directions Mary rang off. She looked at the phone still held tight in her white nuckles.
"It sounds like a panther," she whispered to herself. "But surly not in Norfolk…"

Mary was in her car travelling along a bumpy windy country lane. Evening was closing in and the tree branches hung across the road. Mary kept her eyes ahead of her, all her senses were tuned in to the fields around, wondering if a dark shape lerked behind the hedges. She felt nervous but exited at the same time. She knew that the panther was one of the most dangerous wild cats you could get but also one of the most beautiful with itss jet black fur and red eyes like gleaming rubys.

Her car screeched to a halt outside a tumbledown farmhouse which must be Ed Pitleys farm. As she got out of her car streching her stiff musles the door creeked open and a tall figure stood there. He had a shotgun over his sholder.

"You must be Mary Murphy," he said in a short way, "I'm glad you made it tonight. I want to hunt this creature and get it off my land dead or alive."

Mary held out her hand to shake his one, trying to keep him calm or he might end up shooting a rare beautiful animal.

"Pleased to meet you Mr Pitley," she said quietly but firmly. " Please lead the way." Together they walked behind the farmhouse to the field, the field where Ed had seen the strange animal only last night…

This piece of writing has some clear features of a mystery story, eg. building of atmosphere and tension, introduction of main character and realistic dialogue.

It gives insight into the main character's thoughts and feelings.

The story holds the reader's attention with a good balance between dialogue and description. The opening gets the reader into the story immediately and the ending points the way to the next chapter in a 'cliff-hanger' style, using ellipsis (…) for suspense.

Paragraphs are usually linked together clearly to show the sequence of events ('When Ed finished…') but this is not always the case ('Mary was in her car…').

A range of sentence types and structures is used, though there are some very long sentences which could be punctuated more clearly. However, direct speech is punctuated accurately.

This answer has been given a mark of 14/30, at the top of the Level 5 mark range.

Sample answer for Writing paper 2: Shorter task

Hello everyone. As we all know, Year Council representatives are meeting today to decide which prize Year Nine will accept from the judges of the 'Techno-school' competition. Like the other Form Reps, I will attempt to weigh up the advantages and disadvantages of each prize so that we can come to a decision at the end of the meeting.

Firstly, the day trip to Wyton Towers. What are the advantages of this prize?
Well obviously it's an exciting place to visit and we get a day off from lessons too. More seriously though, it's an attraction which is very expensive. Not everyone can afford to go there, especially if the whole family goes. If we accept this prize it gives everyone in the Year, whatever their financial circomstances, the oppurtunity to experience the thrills and spills of the rides.

However, this prize has disadvantages too. Wyton Towers is two hours drive from school. This means that we will waste four precious hours of our winning day sitting in a coach. Secondly, although we might like the idea of missing school, some parents might complain that we are losing valuable lesson time especially in the lead up to SATs.

Next I will consider the Christmas party. What are the advantages of accepting this prize? One argument is that it would help the Year to socialise. Our school is very large and not everyone in the year knows each other but a party would give everyone the chance to mix in an enviroment outside the classroom. Another point is that it would take place at school and therefore we could make the most of our time rather than spending it travelling.

The main disadvantage of this prize, as far as I can see, is that some people may not regard it as 'special' enough because we are not going out of school.

I hope I have given you a clear picture of some of the pros and cons of these two prizes. Both are worth winning, but which one will be chosen? It's up to us to decide!
Thank you for listening.

The speech is appropriate to the context and the listeners. An objective viewpoint is maintained throughout the piece and different viewpoints are given. ('some parents might complain…')

The piece is very clearly structured with an appropriate beginning and end together with links between paragraphs ('Firstly….However…Next…').

Ideas within paragraphs are linked by balancing advantages against disadvantages .

Attempts have been made to vary the length and type of sentence to create a particular effect, eg. the use of questions. Impersonal form used to convey an objective viewpoint ('One argument is that…').

A range of punctuation is used, usually accurately.

Most spelling, including that of irregular words, is correct, though there are a few mistakes ('circomstances, oppurtunity, enviroment').

This piece has been given a mark of 12/20, in the middle of the Level 6 mark range.

Working out your National Curriculum level

If you want to get a rough idea of your overall NC Level for Writing, add your marks together for the Longer and Shorter tasks. You should then have a mark out of 50. Use the chart below to convert this mark to a NC Level.

Mark	Level
33-50	7
24-32	6
14-23	5
7-13	4
0-6	Below 4

Marking the Shakespeare paper

The marking grid on the next page will give you an idea of the criteria used for assessing the Shakespeare paper.

National Curriculum levels given are a rough guide only. It is much more important that you discuss your written answer with a parent or friend, focusing on what you have done well and how you could improve.

The task is designed to assess your reading ability and is therefore not marked for grammar, spelling or punctuation. However, you should try to write as accurately as possible in order to get your points across clearly.

Reading criteria	Marks	NC Level
The answer will give a few simple facts and opinions about Lady Macbeth's feelings, eg. in the first extract "she gets angry with Macbeth" and in the second "she seems more nervous". There may be some misunderstandings. The answer will tend to retell the story without taking the director's point of view.	0-4	Below 4
The answer will show a general understanding of the character's feelings, eg. "she tries her hardest to persuade Macbeth to continue with the plan". There will be some limited advice given to the actor playing Lady Macbeth, eg. "she should speak sharply to her husband" but this will not be sustained.	5-7	4
There will be some comments on how the actor can show Lady Macbeth's different moods, eg. in the first extract "she should speak quickly and intensely to show how much she wants to change his mind" and in the second "she could show how anxious she is by looking over her shoulder all the time". Advice to the actor shows some understanding of Lady Macbeth's use of language, eg "she asks Macbeth lots of questions to help persuade him". Points are supported by quotation or reference to the text.	8-11	5
The answer will show a clear focus on Lady Macbeth's changing moods and how the actor might show these on stage, eg." she is desperate to change his mind, so she uses emotional blackmail to question both his love for her and his manliness: 'When you durst do it, then you were a man'. She could say these lines with a sneer in her voice, as if she despises her husband". The answer is developed and points are justified by well-chosen references to the text.	12-14	6
A detailed interpretation of the role of Lady Macbeth in these scenes, showing insight into her changing feelings and how the actor could show them by tone of voice, body language and gesture. Eg. "At the beginning of the second extract she appears fearless but her jumpiness when she hears a noise proves that this is bravado. The actor should show the difference between her inner and outer feelings by switching between a bold manner and quick, staccato questions." There is a clear appreciation of the effect of language, eg. "the maternal words she uses: 'given suck…tender…babe' is a shocking contrast to the violent image of 'dash'd the brains out' showing how resolved she is to fulfil their plan". The whole answer is closely and precisely linked to the text.	15-18	7

MACBETH	Hark! Who lies i' the second chamber?
LADY MACBETH	Donalbain.
MACBETH	*[Looking on his hands]* This is a sorry sight. 20
LADY MACBETH	A foolish thought, to say a sorry sight.
MACBETH	There's one did laugh in's sleep, and one cried 'Murder!' That they did wake each other: I stood and heard them: But they did say their prayers, and address'd them Again to sleep. 25
LADY MACBETH	There are two lodged together.
MACBETH	One cried 'God bless us!' and 'Amen' the other; As they had seen me with these hangman's hands. Listening their fear, I could not say 'Amen,' When they did say 'God bless us!'
LADY MACBETH	Consider it not so deeply.
MACBETH	But wherefore could not I pronounce 'Amen'? 30 I had most need of blessing, and 'Amen' Stuck in my throat.
LADY MACBETH	These deeds must not be thought After these ways; so, it will make us mad.
MACBETH	Methought I heard a voice cry 'Sleep no more! Macbeth does murder sleep', the innocent sleep, 35 Sleep that knits up the ravell'd sleeve of care, The death of each day's life, sore labour's bath, Balm of hurt minds, great nature's second course, Chief nourisher in life's feast,–
LADY MACBETH	What do you mean?
MACBETH	Still it cried 'Sleep no more!' to all the house: 40 'Glamis hath murder'd sleep, and therefore Cawdor Shall sleep no more; Macbeth shall sleep no more.'
LADY MACBETH	Who was it that thus cried? Why, worthy thane, You do unbend your noble strength, to think So brainsickly of things. Go get some water, 45 And wash this filthy witness from your hand. Why did you bring these daggers from the place? They must lie there: go carry them; and smear The sleepy grooms with blood.

Shakespeare: Macbeth

MACBETH   I'll go no more:
                    I am afraid to think what I have done;   50
                    Look on't again I dare not.

LADY MACBETH   Infirm of purpose!
                    Give me the daggers: the sleeping and the dead
                    Are but as pictures: 'tis the eye of childhood
                    That fears a painted devil. If he do bleed,
                    I'll gild the faces of the grooms withal;   55
                    For it must seem their guilt.

Exit. Knocking within

MACBETH   Whence is that knocking?
                    How is't with me, when every noise appals me?
                    What hands are here? ha! they pluck out mine eyes.
                    Will all great Neptune's ocean wash this blood
                    Clean from my hand? No, this my hand will rather   60
                    The multitudinous seas in incarnadine,
                    Making the green one red.

Re-enter LADY MACBETH

LADY MACBETH My hands are of your colour; but I shame
                    To wear a heart so white.
Knocking within
                                    I hear a knocking
                    At the south entry: retire we to our chamber;   65
                    A little water clears us of this deed:
                    How easy is it, then! Your constancy
                    Hath left you unattended.
Knocking within
                                    Hark! more knocking.
                    Get on your nightgown, lest occasion call us,
                    And show us to be watchers. Be not lost   70
                    So poorly in your thoughts.

MACBETH   To know my deed, 'twere best not know myself.

Knocking within

                    Wake Duncan with thy knocking! I would thou couldst!

Exeunt

ENGLISH

KEY STAGE 3   LEVELS 4 – 7

READING PAPER 2

Remember

To complete this test you will need a watch or clock to time yourself.

Sit at a table in a quiet place.

The next five pages contain three extracts on the theme of 'Facing the Elements'.

- You should spend 15 minutes reading these extracts before turning to the questions on pages 29 to 34.

- After you have read the extracts through, you have one hour to answer the questions.

- There are spaces in which you should write your answers, but you can use extra paper if you need it.

- The paper has 32 marks in total.

In 1911 Captain Robert Scott sailed to Antarctica in an attempt to beat the Norwegian explorer Amundsen to the South Pole. The expedition was a disastrous one. Scott and his four companions reached the Pole on January 16th to find that Amundsen had reached it 32 days earlier. Scott and his four companions had to make the long journey back to their base camp with very little food. The weather was terrible and the men suffered from scurvy (a disease caused by malnutrition) and frostbite.

The following extracts are taken from Captain Scott's diary.

Saturday, February 17 - A very terrible day. Evans looked a little better after a good sleep, and declared, as he always did, that he was quite well. He started in his place on the traces, but half an hour later worked his ski shoes adrift, and had to leave the sledge. The surface was awful, the soft recently fallen snow clogging the ski and runners at every step, the sledge groaning, the sky overcast, and the land hazy. We stopped after about one hour, and Evans came up again, but very slowly. Half an hour later he dropped out again on the same plea. He asked Bowers to lend him a piece of string. I cautioned him to come on as quickly as he could, and he answered cheerfully as I thought. We had to push on, and the remainder of us were forced to pull very hard, sweating heavily. Abreast the Monument Rock we stopped, and seeing Evans a long way astern, I camped for lunch. There was no alarm at first, and we prepared tea and our own meal, consuming the latter.

After lunch, and Evans still not appearing, we looked out, to see him still afar off. By this time we were alarmed, and all four started back on ski. I was first to reach the poor man and shocked at his appearance; he was on his knees with clothing disarranged, hands uncovered and frostbitten, and a wild look in his eyes. Asked what was the matter, he replied with a slow speech that he didn't know, but thought he must have fainted. We got him on his feet, but after two or three steps he sank down again. He showed every sign of complete collapse. Wilson, Bowers, and I went back for the sledge, whilst Oates remained with him. When we returned he was practically unconscious, and when we got him into the tent quite comatose. He died quietly at 12.30 A.M.

On discussing the symptoms we think he began to get weaker just before we reached the Pole, and that his downward path was accelerated first by the shock of his frostbitten fingers, and later by falls during rough travelling on the glacier, further by his loss of all confidence in himself. Wilson thinks it certain he must have injured his brain by a fall.

It is a terrible thing to lose a companion in this way, but calm reflection shows that there could not have been a better ending to the terrible anxieties of the past week. Discussion of the situation at lunch yesterday shows us what a desperate pass we were in with a sick man on our hands at such a distance from home.

Friday, March 16 or Saturday 17 - Lost track of dates, but think the last correct. Tragedy all along the line. At lunch, the day before yesterday, poor Titus Oates said he couldn't go on; he proposed we should leave him in his sleeping-bag. That we could not do, and we induced him to come on, on the afternoon march. In spite of its awful nature for him he struggled on and we made a few miles. At night he was worse and we knew the end had come.

Should this be found I want these facts recorded. Oates' last thoughts were of his Mother, but immediately before he took pride in thinking that his regiment would be pleased with the bold way in which he met his death. We can testify to his bravery. He has borne intense suffering for weeks without complaint, and to the very last was able and willing to discuss outside subjects. He did not - would not - give up hope till the very end. He was a brave soul. This was the end. He slept through the night before last, hoping not to wake; but he woke in the morning - yesterday. It was blowing a blizzard. He said, 'I am just going outside and may be some time.' He went out into the blizzard and we have not seen him since.

Final Entries
Wednesday, March 21 - Got within 11 miles of depot Monday night; had to lay up all yesterday in severe blizzard. To-day forlorn hope, Wilson and Bowers going to depot for fuel.

Thursday, March 22 and 23 - Blizzard bad as ever - Wilson and Bowers unable to start - to-morrow last chance - no fuel and only one or two of food left - must be near the end. Have decided it shall be natural - we shall march for the depot with or without our effects and die in our tracks.

Thursday, March 29 - Since the 21st we have had a continuous gale from W.S.W. and S.W. We had fuel to make two cups of tea apiece and bare food for two days on the 20th. Every day we have been ready to start for our depot 11 miles away, but outside the door of the tent it remains a scene of whirling drift. I do not think we can hope for any better things now. We shall stick it out to the end, but we are getting weaker, of course, and the end cannot be far. It seems a pity, but I do not think I can write more.
R. Scott

Last entry
For God's sake look after our people.

This extract is taken from a short story called 'To Build A Fire, written by the American author Jack London. The story is set in the early twentieth century in northern Canada. In the winter, this area becomes dangerously cold – so cold that a man could freeze to death if he is not careful. The story is about a newcomer to this area who sets out on a trip hoping to find a way to send logs down the Yukon river once spring comes and the ice melts. He has been warned not to travel alone in such cold conditions, but he goes anyway, with only his dog for company. The story begins as they are hurrying back to their camp and the man's friends. As time goes on the man begins to worry about the dangers of cold and frostbite. He stops to have lunch and build a fire.

At half-past twelve, to the minute, he arrived at the forks of the creek. He was pleased at the speed he had made. If he kept it up, he would certainly be with the boys by six. He unbuttoned his jacket and shirt and drew forth his lunch. The action consumed no more than a quarter of a minute, yet in that brief moment the numbness laid hold of the exposed fingers. He did not put the mitten on, but, instead, struck the fingers a dozen sharp smashes against his leg. Then he sat down on a snow-covered log to eat.

The sting that followed upon the striking of his fingers against his leg ceased so quickly that he was startled, he had had no chance to take a bite of biscuit. He struck the fingers repeatedly and returned them to the mitten, baring the other hand for the purpose of eating. He tried to take a mouthful, but the **ice-muzzle** prevented. He had forgotten to build a fire and thaw out. He chuckled at his foolishness, and as he chuckled he noted the numbness creeping into the exposed fingers. Also, he noted that the stinging which had first come to his toes when he sat down was already passing away. He wondered whether the toes were warm or numbed. He moved them inside the **moccasins** and decided that they were numbed. He pulled the mitten on hurriedly and stood up. He was a bit frightened. He stamped up and down until the stinging returned into the feet.

It certainly was cold, was his thought. That man from Sulphur Creek had spoken the truth when telling how cold it sometimes got in the country. And he had laughed at him at the time! That showed one must not be too sure of things. There was no mistake about it, it was cold. He strode up and down, stamping his feet and **threshing** his arms, until reassured by the returning warmth. Then he got out matches and proceeded to make a fire. From the undergrowth, where high water of the previous spring had lodged a supply of seasoned twigs, he got his firewood. Working carefully from a small beginning, he soon had a roaring fire, over which he thawed the ice from his face and in the protection of which he ate his biscuits. For the moment the cold of space was outwitted. The dog took satisfaction in the fire, stretching out close enough for warmth and far enough away to escape being singed. When the man had finished, he filled his pipe and took his comfortable time over a smoke. Then he pulled on his mittens, settled the ear-flaps of his cap firmly about his ears, and took the creek trail up the left fork. The dog was disappointed and **yearned** back toward the fire. This man did not know cold. Possibly all the generations of his ancestry had been ignorant of cold, of real cold, of cold one hundred and seven degrees below freezing-point. But the dog knew; all its ancestry knew, and it had inherited the knowledge. And it knew that it was not good to walk abroad in such fearful cold. It was the time to lie snug in a hole in the snow and wait for a curtain of cloud to be drawn across the face of outer space whence this cold came...

There did not seem to be so many springs on the left fork of the Henderson, and for half an hour the man saw no signs of any. And then it happened. At a place where there were no signs, where the soft, unbroken snow seemed to advertise solidity beneath, the man broke through. It was not deep. He wetted himself half-way to the knees before he floundered out to the firm crust. He was angry, and cursed his luck aloud. He had hoped to get into camp with the boys at six o'clock, and this would delay him an hour, for he would have to build a fire and dry out his foot-gear. This was **imperative** at that low temperature - he knew that much; and he turned aside to the bank, which he climbed. On top, tangled in the underbrush about the trunks of several small spruce trees, was a high-water deposit of dry firewood--sticks and twigs principally, but also larger portions of seasoned branches and fine, dry, last-year's grasses. He threw down several large pieces on top of the snow. This served for a foundation and prevented the young flame from drowning itself in the snow it otherwise would melt. The flame he got by touching a match to a small shred of birch-bark that he took from his pocket. This burned even more readily than paper. Placing it on the foundation, he fed the young flame with wisps of dry grass and with the tiniest dry twigs. He worked slowly and carefully, keenly aware of his danger.

Gradually, as the flame grew stronger, he increased the size of the twigs with which he fed it. He squatted in the snow, pulling the twigs out from their entanglement in the brush and feeding directly to the flame. He knew there must be no failure. When it is seventy- five below zero, a man must not fail in his first attempt to build a fire - that is, if his feet are wet. If his feet are dry, and he fails, he can run along the trail for half a mile and restore his circulation. But the circulation of wet and freezing feet cannot be restored by running when it is seventy-five below. No matter how fast he runs, the wet feet will freeze the harder. All this the man knew. The old-timer on Sulphur Creek had told him about it the previous fall, and now he was appreciating the advice. Already all sensation had gone out of his feet.

But he was safe. Toes and nose and cheeks would be only touched by the frost, for the fire was beginning to burn with strength. He was feeding it with twigs the size of his finger. In another minute he would be able to feed it with branches the size of his wrist, and then he could remove his wet foot-gear, and, while it dried, he could keep his naked feet warm by the fire, rubbing them at first, of course, with snow. The fire was a success. He was safe. He remembered the advice of the old-timer on Sulphur Creek, and smiled. The old-timer had been very serious in laying down the law that no man must travel alone in the Klondike after fifty below. Well, here he was; he had had the accident; he was alone; and he had saved himself. Those old-timers were rather womanish, some of them, he thought. All a man had to do was to keep his head, and he was all right. Any man who was a man could travel alone. But it was surprising, the rapidity with which his cheeks and nose were freezing. And he had not thought his fingers could go lifeless in so short a time. Lifeless they were, for he could scarcely make them move together to grip a twig, and they seemed remote from his body and from him. When he touched a twig, he had to look and see whether or not he had hold of it. The wires were pretty well down between him and his finger-ends. All of which counted for little. There was the fire, snapping and crackling and promising life with every dancing flame. He started to untie his moccasins. They were coated with ice; the thick German socks were like sheaths of iron half-way to the knees; and the moccasin strings were like rods of steel all twisted and knotted as by some **conflagration**. For a moment he tugged with his numbed fingers, then, realizing the **folly** of it, he drew his sheath-knife. But before he could cut the strings, it happened. It was his own fault or, rather, his mistake. He should not have built the fire under the spruce tree. He should have built it in the open. But it had been easier to pull the twigs from the brush and drop them directly on the fire. Now the tree under which he had done this carried a weight of snow on its boughs. No wind had blown for weeks, and each bough was fully **freighted**. Each time he had pulled a twig he had communicated a slight agitation to the tree–an imperceptible agitation, so far as he was concerned, but an agitation sufficient to bring about the disaster. High up in the tree one bough capsized its load of snow. This fell on the boughs beneath, capsizing them. This process continued, spreading out and involving the whole tree. It grew like an avalanche, and it descended without warning upon the man and the fire, and the fire was blotted out! Where it had burned was a mantle of fresh and disordered snow. The man was shocked. It was as though he had just heard his own sentence of death.

ice-muzzle – the man's beard and moustache have frozen, so that he cannot move his mouth very easily.   **moccasins** - shoes   **threshing** - shaking   **yearned** - looked back longingly   **imperative** – most important   **conflagration** – fierce fire   **folly** - foolishness   **freighted** – weighed down

Wilfred Owen was one of the most famous poets who wrote about their experiences in the First World War. He was killed in action in 1918 at the age of twenty-five.

The text which follows is an abridged (shortened) version of his poem 'Exposure', in which he writes about waiting in the trenches for battle to begin during winter time.

Exposure

Our brains ache, in the merciless iced east winds that knife us . . .
Wearied we keep awake because the night is silent . . .
Low drooping flares confuse our memory of **the salient** . . .
Worried by silence, sentries whisper, curious, nervous,
But nothing happens.

Watching, we hear the mad gusts tugging on the wire.
Like twitching agonies of men among its brambles.
Northward, **incessantly**, the flickering gunnery rumbles,
Far off, like a dull rumour of some other war.
What are we doing here?

The **poignant** misery of dawn begins to grow . . .
We only know war lasts, rain soaks, and clouds sag stormy.
Dawn massing in the east her **melancholy** army
Attacks once more in ranks on shivering ranks of gray,
But nothing happens.

Sudden successive flights of bullets streak the silence.
Less deadly than the air that shudders black with snow,
With sidelong flowing flakes that flock, pause and renew,
We watch them wandering up and down the wind's **nonchalance**,
But nothing happens.

To-night, **His** frost will fasten on this mud and us,
Shrivelling many hands and puckering foreheads crisp.
The burying-party, picks and shovels in their shaking grasp,
Pause over half-known faces. All their eyes are ice,
But nothing happens.

the salient – another name for the front line of trenches   **incessantly** – without stopping

poignant – emotionally moving   **melancholy** – sad   **nonchalance** – carelessness

His – God's

1   In the entry for Saturday February 17, Scott describes the sledge as 'groaning'.

_____

_____

1 mark

2   In the same entry, Scott describes the gradual worsening of Evans' condition. Identify four phrases from the first paragraph of this entry (from 'A very terrible'…to '12.30 A.M.') which explain this and complete the stages below.

Stage 1   'Evans looked a little better after a good sleep.'

Stage 2   _____

Stage 3   _____

Stage 4   _____

Stage 5   _____

2 marks

Stage 6   'He died quietly at 12.30 A.M.'

3   How does the last paragraph of the entry for Saturday February 17 (from 'It is a terrible thing'…to 'from home') make the reader think that Scott feels both saddened and relieved by Evans' death?

(a) Pick one phrase or sentence that shows that Scott is saddened.

_____

(b) Pick one phrase or sentence that shows he is relieved.

_____

2 marks

4   The style of the final entries is different from the style of the previous entries.

(a) Explain one difference in the way they are written.

_____

_____

(b) What is the effect of this on the reader?

_____

2 marks

_____

5 From the whole text, how does the language of the diary emphasise the harsh conditions of Antarctica, its effects on the explorers and Scott's thoughts and feelings?

You should comment on how words and phrases:

(a) describe the weather;
(b) describe the men's physical and mental condition;
(c) describe Scott's view of events.

5 marks

6   Read the first paragraph again (from 'At half-past twelve...' to 'feet')
What important mistake does the man make?

_____

_____

_____

1 mark

7   From the second paragraph ('It certainly was...' to 'cold came'), identify

(a) one phrase that shows that the man is not experienced in these conditions.

_____

_____

(b) one phrase that shows that the dog is wiser than the man.

_____

_____

2 marks

8   The man falls through the ice and has to build a second fire to dry out his wet feet. The writer describes his thoughts when the fire begins to burn strongly.

'The fire was a success. He was safe. He remembered the advice of the old-timer on Sulphur Creek, and smiled. The old-timer had been very serious in laying down the law that no man must travel in the Klondike after fifty below. Well, here he was; he had had the accident; he was alone; and he had saved himself. Those old-timers were rather womanish, some of them, he thought.'

Write down two things that these lines suggest about the man.

• _____

_____

• _____

_____

2 marks

        Total score for this page:

The man starts to take off his moccasins.
'They were coated with ice; the thick German socks were like **sheaths of iron half-way to the knees**; and the moccasin strings were like **rods of steel all twisted and knotted as by some conflagration**.'

What do the words in bold type suggest about

(a) the man's socks?

_____

_____

(b) the moccasin strings (laces)?

_____

_____

10 How does the writer build up a sense of the danger facing the man from the beginning to the end of this extract?

You should comment on:

(a) the order in which events happen;

(b) the way in which he describes the man's changing feelings about his situation;

(c) the way in which the writer uses language to describe the cold.

_____

_____

_____

_____

_____

_____

_____

_____

_____

_____

_____

_____

_____

_____

_____

_____

_____

_____

_____

_____

_____

_____

_____

5 marks

Questions 11 to 13 are about 'Exposure' on page 28.

11 In the first line of the poem, Owen uses the phrase 'the merciless iced east winds that knife us'.

Explain two things that this phrase suggests about the winds.

_____

_____

_____

_____

2 marks

33

12 Each stanza (verse) of the poem ends with a shorter line. What do these lines suggest about the mood of the soldiers?

The repetition of 'But nothing happens' suggests

_____

_____

_____

The question 'What are we doing here?' suggests

_____

_____

_____

13 What do you learn about the poet's viewpoint and purpose in the poem as a whole?

Decide whether the following statements are true or false and then write T for True or F for False in each of the boxes.

The poet thinks that the weather is more dangerous than the war at this time. ☐

The poet feels happy that there is no fighting at the moment. ☐

The poet's aim is to make his readers feel that the soldiers are safe because there is no fighting. ☐

The poet's aim is to make his readers realise that soldiers are suffering from more than just the effects of battle. ☐

Total score for this page: ☐

ENGLISH

KEY STAGE 3   LEVELS 4 – 7

WRITING PAPER 2

Remember

To complete this test you will need a watch or clock to time yourself.

Sit at a table in a quiet place.

This test contains two writing tasks.

- It is 1 hour and 15 minutes long.

- You should spend 45 minutes on Section 1. This is the longer writing task and is worth 30 marks. We provide a planning sheet but you will need to use sheets of paper or an exercise book to complete the task.

- You should spend 30 minutes on Section 2. This is the shorter writing task. It is worth 20 marks (including 4 marks for spelling).

- Spend the first 15 minutes planning your answer to Section 1 on the planning page provided.

Section 1 Longer writing task

You are writing a mystery novel based on local stories of a huge black animal which roams the countryside.

Below is a newspaper cutting which you intend to use for ideas:

NIGHT BEAST WALKS AGAIN

The mysterious black creature nicknamed 'the Night Beast' by local people was seen again yesterday on the Manford Hills.

Farmer Ed Pitley, who keeps sheep on the hills, was checking his lambs when he saw a dark shape running beside the fence which borders his field.
" It frightened the life out of me," he said.
" I would say it was the size of a lion, definitely too large for a dog. All my sheep started running about and bleating. We have to do something to track this animal down before it does any damage to livestock or even people."

Mary Murphy, a world expert on big cats, has been called in to lead the hunt for the animal.

Write the first chapter of your novel 'The Night Beast'.

(30 marks)

Section 1 Longer writing task
PLANNING PAGE

Use this page to plan your work. It will not be marked.

Notes on description of setting to build up atmosphere

Notes on what happens in this first chapter

Notes on characters to appear and dialogue between them

Writing Paper 2

Section 2 Shorter writing task

Your Year Group has won a competition. You are your form's representative on the Year Council. You receive the following note from your Headteacher:

Congratulations Year Nine!

You have to decide between two prizes for the whole year group:

1. A day trip to Wyton Towers, the local theme park

   or

2. A Christmas party in the evening at school.

   I would like the Year Council to meet to decide which prize will be chosen. Each form representative will make a speech analysing the advantages and disadvantages of each prize and then a vote will be taken.

   Thank you

Write your speech for the Year Council.

(20 marks)   (including 4 for spelling)